RIDDLES

FOR ADULTS

Level: Medium

Over 950 Challenging riddles that twist your mind

Jayde Nguyen

The difficulty of these riddles are somewhere between easy and hard, that is why they are considered moderate.

QUESTION 1-50:

1. What's the red stuff between elephant's toes?
2. There is a kind of fish that can never swim. What is that?
3. What is a Mummy's favorite type of music?
4. What can you catch but not throw?
5. What do you get if you put a radio in the fridge?
6. When young, I am sweet in the sun.
   When middle-aged, I make you gay.
   When old, I am valued more than ever.
7. What's red and bad for your teeth?
8. What is it that no man wants, but no man wants to lose?
9. What does an old tan broken down house wear outside?
10. Weight in my belly, trees on my back. Nails in my ribs, feet I do lack. What am I?
11. Which tree is the most difficult to get along with?
12. What kind of street does a ghost like best?
13. All day long it's in and out. I discharge loads from my shaft. Both men and women go down on me. What am I?
14. I saw a strange creature,
    Long, hard, and straight,
    Thrusting in a round, dark, opening,
    Preparing to discharge its load of lives,
    Puffing and squealing noises accompanied it,
    Then a final screech as it slowed and stopped.
15. What has to be broken before you can use it?
16. Thirty white horses on a red hill,

First they champ,
Then they stamp,
Then they stand still.

17. I am something that floats. But after a period of time I fall.
18. What jumps when it walks and sits when it stands?
19. Two birds, trying to balance in one twig.
20. Tall when seated, short when standing.
21. What's always coming, but never arrives?
22. What loses its head every morning only to get it back every night?
23. Which bow can't be tied?
24. I'm named after nothing, though I'm awfully clamorous. And when I'm not working, your house is less glamorous. What am I?
25. What makes a loud noise when changing its jacket, becomes larger but weighs less?
26. What has ten letters and starts with gas?
27. When it was young, it had a tail. When it grew up, it had knees.
28. What English word retains the same pronunciation, even after you take away four of its five letters?
29. What demands an answer, but asks no question?
30. The more you take from me, the bigger I get. What am I?
31. Although I'm not an insect, some people found me very difficult to exterminate. They called me something like 'insane priest.' The first half of my name means the same as 'scrape,' & my last three letters are a metal. Who am I?
32. A harvest sown and reaped on the same day
In an unplowed field,
Which increases without growing,
Remains whole though it is eaten
Within and without,
Is useless and yet
The staple of nations.
33. I have one eye,

See near and far,
I hold the moments you treasure,
And the things that make you weep.

34. There is a word in the English language in which the first two letters signify a male, the first three letters signify a female, the first four signify a great man, and the whole word, a great woman. What is the word?

35. I look flat, but I am deep,
Hidden realms I shelter.
Lives I take, but food I offer.
At times I am beautiful.
I can be calm, angry and turbulent.
I have no heart, but offer pleasure as well as death.
No man can own me, yet I encompass what all men must have.

36. There's no reason to fear
If you see me lurking here
Even though I shouldn't exist
But few might have missed
That I'm not at all real
Because nothing can conceal
The fact that I'm something
That's not at all living
What am I?

37. Screaming, soaring seeking sky.
Flowers of fire flying high,
Eastern art from ancient time,
Name me now and solve this rhyme.

38. It may only be given,
Not taken or bought,
What the sinner desires,
But the saint does not.

39. I am rather large and usually majestic.
I am every hue of the rainbow
I can eat you, I may heat you,

You only wish you could see me. What am I?

40. I follow the orders of only two.
    I respect the work of only two.
    I am in constant battles with many,
    Though one surpassed them all.
    With forces joined,
    We created hell,
    Until our mutual enemy fell.
    Who am I?

41. A three-letter word I'm sure you know,
    I can be on a boat or a sleigh in the snow,
    I'm pals with the rain and honor a king,
    But my favorite use is attached to a string. What am I?

42. Everyone has it.
    Those who have it least don't know that they have it.
    Those who have it most wish they had less of it,
    But not too little or none at all.

43. As beautiful as the setting sun,
    As delicate as the morning dew;
    An angel's dusting from the stars,
    That can turn the Earth into a frosted moon. What am I?

44. I have a leg but I do not move,
    A face but no expression,
    Be it wind or rain I stay outside. What am I?

45. I have a title and many pages
    I am a genteel of genteel descent
    I am a killer veteran of war
    I am a slave to my lord
    Pledged to his service.

46. Alight or in dark, my face is a leer.
    In a field with my brothers, you'll find me without bother,
    For that autumn day is mine.

47. I'm a word, six letters long; I sometimes enter with a gong.
    All in order from A to Z, I start with the letter B.
    What is the word?

48. I'm a very valuable thing to have.
    Use me right now, you should.
    Yet if you cut off my hindquarters,
    I'd be but a piece of wood.
    What am I?

49. Deep, deep, do they go.
    Spreading out as they go.
    Never needing any air.
    They are sometimes as fine as hair.

50. Large as a mountain, small as a pea,
    Endlessly swimming in a waterless sea.

ANSWER 1-50

1.	slowpygmies	23.	rainbow
2.	deadfish	24.	vacuum cleaner
3.	wrap	25.	popcorn
4.	cold	26.	automobile
5.	cool music	27.	frog
6.	wine	28.	queue
7.	brick	29.	telephone
8.	lawsuit	30.	hole
9.	tan coat	31.	rasputin
10.	ship	32.	war
11.	crab tree	33.	camera
12.	dead end	34.	heroine
13.	elevator	35.	ocean
14.	subway train	36.	ghost
15.	egg	37.	fireworks
16.	teeth	38.	forgiveness
17.	balloon	39.	dragon
18.	kangaroo	40.	peeves
19.	earrings	41.	bow
20.	dog	42.	age
21.	tomorrow	43.	snow
22.	pillow	44.	scarecrow

45.	knight	48.	logic
46.	pumpkin	49.	roots
47.	begins	50.	asteroids

QUESTION 51-100

51. Lovely and round, I shine with pale light,
Grown in the darkness, a lady's delight.

52. My sides are firmly laced about,
Yet nothing is within;
You'll think my head is strange indeed,
Being nothing else but skin.

53. Oh how I love my dancing feet!
They stay together - oh so neat.
And when I want to walk a line,
They all stay together and do double time.
I count them up, ten times or more,
And race on-off, across the floor.

54. Within, I clean all that is bad and is old.
I make juice that's the color of gold.
Should I die, a filter machine would you need assembled to
replace me and beans I resemble.

55. I'm not man's best friend, I'm their enemy,
I can mark your end, yet you do not see me,
I am very small, but very tough,
If you have me, then you have it rough.

56. Faster than a twitch!
Fly with me to the Pitch!
With a seeker, a keeper,
Or a chaser, a beater,
Wizard or witch;
I play a mean game of Quidditch. What am I?

57. Hands she has but does not hold,
teeth she has but does not bite,
feet she has but they are cold,
eyes she has but without sight. Who is she?

58. I go around in circles, But always straight ahead
    Never complain, No matter where I am led.
59. It's in your hand though you cannot feel it.
    Only you and time can reveal it.
60. A serpent swam in a silver urn,
    A golden bird did in its mouth abide,
    The serpent drank the water, this in turn,
    Killed the serpent. Then the gold bird died.
61. Above all things have I been placed
    Thus have I, a man disgraced.
    I describe sunlight or lock
    But after all, I'm just a rock.
62. More precious than gold, but cannot be bought,
    Can never be sold, only earned if it's sought,
    If it is broken it can still be mended,
    At birth it can't start nor by death is it ended.
63. Tool of thief, toy of queen.
    Always used to be unseen.
    Sign of joy, sign of sorrow.
    Giving all likeness borrowed.
64. Flour of England, fruit of Spain,
    Met together in a shower of rain;
    Put in a bag tied round with a string,
    If you'll tell me this riddle, I'll give you a ring.
65. My first is in wield, sever bones and marrow.
    My second is in blade, forged in cold steel.
    My third is in arbalest, and also in arrows.
    My fourth is in power, plunged through a shield.
    My fifth is in honor, and also in vows
    My last will put an end to it all.
66. My coat keeps me safe
    From damage that's near.
    I cause you happiness, sadness,
    Anticipation and fear.
    On the outside, I am put under judgment of price.

But my insides have far more value
That not even MONEY can suffice.

67. I am everywhere.
Nothing can compare.
Run and hide and I will still be there
Because everything is mine to share.
No need to seek me out,
Though, you may just run out. What am I?

68. Not a burden for its weight and daily carried out,
He who takes it wishes it had never come about.

69. Three little letters, a paradox to some.
The worse that it is, the better it becomes.

70. From that which comes within itself,
It builds its table on my shelf.

71. I have no wings but I fly, I have no teeth but I bite. What am I?

72. What do people want the least on their hands?

73. I grow for a surface, even if you cut me. I continue to grow even after death.

74. Blend a teapot shot so the pearlies won't rot!

75. You use a knife to slice my head and weep beside me when I am dead. What am I?

76. You'll have me at night and if you remove the first letter I denote the top, such as on a train.

77. What goes in the water red, and comes out black?

78. What can be right but never wrong?

79. I wear a red coat and have a stone in my throat. What am I?

80. What has feet and legs and nothing else?

81. We chop its feet; we drink its blood.

82. It produces a flower but it is not its fruit; it produces branches which are its fruit.

83. What gets broken without being hold?

84. A fruit on a tree. A tree on a fruit.

85. What is lengthened by being cut at both ends?

86. When they are caught, they are thrown away.

When they escape, you itch all day.

87. You can have it, and be at it,
    But it never lasts forever.
88. When is 1500 plus 20 and 1600 minus 40 the same thing?
89. I have a thousand wheels, but move I do not. Call me what I am, call me a lot.
90. Who is it that rows quickly with four oars but never comes out under his own roof?
91. Not a priest, not a king but wears different kinds of clothes.
92. Today he is there to trip you up and he will torture you tomorrow.
93. What goes through a door but never goes in and never comes out?
94. What can you throw but not catch?
95. Steals an event or even a mood. Reveals the truth or shatters it.
96. It is hate and has hate in it, but it isn't hate.
97. What is never used unless it's in a tight place?
98. Although my cow is dead, I still beat her. What a racket she makes!
99. Just head and foot yet never tires of dancing.
100. What kinds of men are always above board?

ANSWER 51-100

51.	pearl	62.	friendship
52.	drum	63.	mask
53.	centipede	64.	plum pudding
54.	kidney	65.	weapon
55.	virus	66.	book
56.	broom	67.	space
57.	doll	68.	punishment
58.	wheel	69.	pun
59.	fate	70.	spider
60.	oil lamp	71.	bullet
61.	moon	72.	handcuffs

73.	human hair	87.	peace
74.	toothpaste	88.	military time
75.	onion	89.	parking lot
76.	supper	90.	turtle
77.	iron	91.	clothesline
78.	right angle	92.	alcohol
79.	cherry	93.	keyhole
80.	stockings	94.	party
81.	sugarcane	95.	camera
82.	sweet corn	96.	hatred
83.	promise	97.	cork
84.	pineapple	98.	drum
85.	ditch	99.	spinning top
86.	fleas	100.	chessmen

QUESTION 101 – 150:

101. What can burn the eyes, sting the mouth, yet be consumed and thought delicious?
102. What can be swallowed, but can swallow you?
103. A tree with 5 branches, no leaves and no fruits.
104. I am nothing but holes tied to holes, yet am strong as iron.
105. Poorly behaved children often find themselves sitting in these.
106. I end and begin the day,
Without me, you'll pay.
With the aid of sheep,
All my benefits you shall reap.
If I make you miss class,
You shall not pass! What am I?
107. People buy me to eat, but never eat me. What am I?
108. I never ask questions, but I am always answered. What am I?
109. It is sharp but not pepper; white but not paper; green but not shaddock. What am I?

110. A long snake that smokes. What am I?
111. A skin have I, more eyes than one. I can be very nice when I am done. What am I?
112. Until I am measured, I am not known. Yet how you miss me when I have flown. What am I?
113. Ne'er the same,
    In multitude you see me.
    You love me, you hate me, What am I?
114. There are two meanings to me. With one I may need to be broken, with the other I hold on. My favorite characteristic is my charming dimple. What am I?
115. A very pretty thing I am, fluttering in the pale-blue sky. Delicate, fragile on the wing, indeed I am a pretty thing. What am I?
116. I can be told and can make you crazy. Most people don't like me and think I'm harmful. What am I?
117. I have many ears, this may be true
    But no matter how you shout,
    I'll never hear you. What am I?
118. I fall with the waves, rise with the tide, and drift with the current alongside. What am I?
119. I am one of many,
    You forget I'm here, but I'm just below.
    Without me, you'd surely topple,
    Go ahead, what am I?
120. I have four wings, but cannot fly,
    I never laugh and never cry;
    on the same spot I'm always found,
    toiling away with little sound. What am I?
121. I'm a king that speaks for my country
    At birth I protected by no one
    As I grow my father gives me 2 soldiers to protect me
    As I get matured many more are given to me
    And at my full age my father gives me 32 white soldiers to guard me and protect me

What am I?

122. Two bodies with ribs, exposed. What am I?

123. I have no brain but am still smarter than the average human. What am I?

124. I am not alive but I grow. I don't have lungs but I need air. What am i?

125. I go around all the places; cities, towns and villages, but never come inside. What am I?

126. I have no life, but I can die, what am I?

127. Three or four,
I can stab through or rule the seas.
You know my cousins. What am I?

128. I can bring tears to your eyes; resurrect the dead, make you smile, and reverse time. I form in an instant but I last a lifetime. What am I?

129. You can see nothing else when you look in my face,
I will look you in the eye and I will never lie.
What am I?

130. I am flora, not fauna,
I am foliage, not trees,
I am shrubbery, not grass, What am I?

131. I am a strong as ten men
Yet ten men cannot stand me up. What am I?

132. You may always chase me but you are always about 3 miles away. What am I?

133. From house to house I go, sometimes narrow, sometimes wide. And whether there's rain or snow I always stay outside. What am I?

134. Not born, but from a Mother's body drawn, I hang until half of me is gone. I sleep in a cave until I grow old, then valued for my hardened gold. What am I?

135. Half of the population uses me, and you lose me all the time. I'm small and yellow, black, brown or silver.
You use me to hold things up. What am I?

136. Ten Men's Strength, Ten Men's Length,

Ten Men can't break it, yet a young boy walks off with it
What am I?

137. I only have one entrance, but you can come out with three exits. What am I?

138. I have a mouth on my head and eat everything. What am I?

139. I'm lighter than air but a million men can't lift me. What am I?

140. If you eat me, my sender will eat you. What am I?

141. I am used to bat with, yet I never get a hit. I am near a ball, yet it is never thrown. What am I?

142. I know a thousand faces, and count the tailed heads, feasting bright upon the eyes, of many who have died. Wielding well a mighty power, who hath but humble stature. Masses fall upon their knees, to scarce behold my only side. What am I?

143. Many have heard me, but nobody has seen me, and I will not speak back until spoken to. What am I?

144. I fly, yet I have no wings. I cry, yet I have no eyes. Darkness follows me; lower light I never see. What am I?

145. If a man carried my burden, he would break his back.
I am not rich, but I leave silver in my track. What am I?

146. You will always find me in the past.
I can be created in the present,
But the future can never taint me. What am I?

147. It has a long neck,
A name of a bird,
Feeds on cargo of ships,
It's not alive. What am I?

148. Shoot at me a thousand times and I may still survive; one scratch from you and me will find your prospects take a dive. What am I?

149. With me you are blind,
To others and what they are,
Over me you cannot see,
Even though I'm in your head,
I am full of myself,

I think I'm better than you,
I'm a horrible thing to be,
Can you tell me, What am I?

150. Many shapes, many sizes. Can't be seen, only felt. I bring pain, I bring joy, I bring laughter, I bring happiness. I can tear the mightiest from their thrones, and those who have me are rich. What am I?

ANSWER 101 – 150:

101. salt	126. battery
102. pride	127. fork
103. arm	128. memory
104. chain	129. reflection
105. corners	130. bush
106. sleep	131. water
107. plate	132. horizon
108. doorbell	133. path
109. radish	134. cheese
110. train	135. bobby pins
111. potato	136. rope
112. time	137. blouse
113. snowflakes	138. backpack
114. tie	139. bubble
115. butterfly	140. fishhook
116. lie	141. eyelashes
117. cornfield	142. coin
118. plankton	143. echo
119. toes	144. cloud
120. windmill	145. snail
121. tongue	146. history
122. ladder	147. crane
123. calculator	148. eight ball
124. fire	149. ignorance
125. street	150. love

QUESTION 151-200:

151. I have many feathers to help me fly.
     I have a body and head, but I'm not alive.
     It is your strength that determines how far I go.
     You can hold me in your, but I'm never thrown. What am I?
152. A house with two occupants, sometimes one, rarely three.
     Break the walls, eat the borders, then throw away me. What
     am I?
153. Round as an apple, deep as a cup, and all the kings' horses
     can't fill it up. What is it?
154. Thousands of these come together to make a digital image.
     What is it?
155. The sharp slim blade, that cuts the wind. What is it?
156. It's got twists and turns, but has no curves. Twist it to fix it,
     turn it to ruin it. What is it?
157. A home of wood in a wooded place, but built not by hand.
     High above the earthen ground, it holds its pale blue gems.
     What is it?
158. It can be cracked, It can be made,
     It can be told, it can be played. What is it?
159. There was a green house. Inside the green house there was a
     white house. Inside the white house there was a red house.
     Inside the red house there were lots of babies. What is it?
160. MT_TF_S What are the missing letters? Why?
161. George, Helen, and Steve are drinking coffee. Bert, Karen,
     and Dave are drinking soda. Is Elizabeth drinking coffee or
     soda?
162. If 5 cats catch 5 mice in 5 minutes, how long will it take one
     cat to catch a mouse?
163. I'm simple for a few people.
     But hard for them to hear.

I live inside of secrets.

I bring people's worst fears. What am I?

164. What is neither inside the house nor outside the house but a necessity for any home?

165. Which bird does not belong in this group? Finch, gull, eagle, ostrich, or sparrow?

166. We travelled the sea far and wide. At one time, two of my sailors were standing on opposite sides of the ship. One was looking west and the other one east. And at the same time, they could see each other clearly. How can that be possible?

167. A man is trapped in a room. The room has only two possible exits: two doors. Through the first door there is a room constructed from magnifying glass. The blazing hot sun instantly fries anything or anyone that enters. Through the second door there is a fire-breathing dragon. How does the man escape?

168. What animal has no wings, but yet will fly?

169. Two people are born at the same moment, but they don't have the same birthdays. How could this be?

170. In the Tour de France, what is the position of a rider, after he passes the second placed rider?

171. Matt is the fiftieth fastest and the fiftieth slowest runner in his school. Assuming no two runners are the same speed, how many runners are in Matt's school?

172. Lynn likes grapes but not potatoes. She likes squash but not lettuce, and she likes peas but not onions. Following the same rule, will she like pumpkins or apples?

173. Can you guess the next letter in the series? "CYGTNLIT"

174. Susan and Lisa decided to play tennis against each other. They bet $1 on each game they played. Susan won three bets and Lisa won $5. How many games did they play?

175. There is a boat with a ladder attached to it, the ladder is eight feet tall. If the water rises four feet how much of the ladder will be on top of the water?

176. A bat and a ball cost $1.10. The bat costs one dollar more than the ball. How much does the ball cost?

177. When I take five and add six, I get eleven, but when I take six and add seven, I get one. What am I?

178. Joe has ten coins totaling $1.19. From these coins, he cannot make exact change for a dollar, half-dollar, quarter, dime, or nickel. What are the coins?

179. Dean Sam and Castiel are three brothers. Interestingly their current age is prime. What's more interesting that difference between their ages is also prime. How old are they?

180. If you toss a coin 10 times and it lands heads up every time, what are the chances it will land heads up if you toss it again?

181. How can you add eight 8's to get the number 1000?

182. Mr. Smith has 4 daughters. Each of his daughters has a brother. How many children does Mr. Smith have?

183. There are 25 red balls, 47 green balls and 3 blue balls in a basket. There is a blind man. What is the minimum number of balls that the blind man has to pick to make sure that there are at least 2 balls of different colors?

184. Place three matches on a table. Tell a friend to add two more matches to make eight.

185. When my father was 31 I was 8. Now he is twice as old as me. How old am I?

186. My daughter has many sisters. She has as many sisters as she has brothers. Each of her brothers has twice as many sisters as brothers. How many sons and daughters do I have?

187. In a bicycle race, the man who came two places in front of the last man finished one ahead of the man who came fifth. How many contestants were there?

188. An apple is 40 cents, a banana is 60 cents and a grapefruit is 80 cents. How much is a pear?

189. All about, but cannot be seen,
Can be captured, cannot be held,
No throat, but can be heard. Who am I?

190. The more you have of me, the less you see. Who am I?
191. I always run but never walk, often murmur, never talk, have a bed but never sleep, have a mouth but never eat. Who am I?
192. A box without hinges, lock or key, yet golden treasure lies within. Who am I?
193. I give milk and have a horn but I'm not a cow. Who am I?
194. You throw me out when you want to use me and you take me in when you don't want to use me. Who am I?
195. You can hold it without using your hands or your arms. What is it?
196. What tastes better than it smells?
197. What cannot talk but will always reply when spoken to?
198. Take away my first letter, then take away my second letter. Then take away the rest of my letters, yet I remain the same. What am I?
199. It belongs to you, but other people use it more than you do. What is it?
200. What breaks on the water but never on the land?

ANSWER 151-200:

151. arrow
152. peanut
153. well
154. pixel
155. grass
156. Rubik's cube
157. nest
158. joke
159. watermelon
160. W and S for days of the week
161. Elizabeth is drinking coffee. The letter E appears twice in her name, as it does in the names of the others that are drinking coffee.
162. Five minutes.

163. The truth.
164. indows
165. The Ostrich. It doesn't fly.
166. The sailors had their backs against either ends of the ship.
167. He waits until night time and then goes through the first door.
168. A caterpillar has no wings, but will fly when it matures and becomes a butterfly.
169. They are born in different time zones.
170. Second. If you answered first you were wrong. He needs to pass the first placed rider to be first.
171. There are 99 runners in Matt's school.
172. Pumpkins. Lynn only likes things that grow on vines.
173. CYGTNLITS = Can you guess the next letter in the series.
174. They played eleven games.
175. Eight feet, the ladder is attached to the boat.
176. The ball costs 5c. Not 10c. One dollar more than 10c is $1.10, $1.10 + 10c is $1.20 One dollar more than 5c is $1.05. The sum of which is $1.10.
177. Clock
178. A half-dollar, a quarter, four dimes, and four pennies.
179. Sam: 2; Dean: 5; Castiel: 7. Age diff 7 - 2 = '5' is prime; 7 - 5 = '2' is prime; 5 - 2 = '3' is prime.
180. There is a 50/50 chance of each toss being either heads or tails. The previous toss does not impact the next toss.
181. 888+88+8+8+8=1000
182. Five
183. 48 balls. There is a small chance he may pick up 47 green balls in a row.
184. Add two matches to make a roman numeral eight.
185. I must be 23 if my father is twice as old as me.
186. Four daughters and three sons. Each daughter has 3 sisters and 3 brothers, and each brother has 2 brothers and 4 sisters.
187. There were 6 contestants. The man came in 4th place.

188. 40 cents. The price of each fruit is calculated by multiplying the number of vowels by 20c.
189. wind
190. darkness
191. river
192. egg
193. milk truck
194. anchor
195. Your breath.
196. tongue
197. echo
198. postman
199. name
200. wave

QUESTION 201 – 250:

201. The sun bakes them,
     The hand breaks them,
     The foot treads them,
     The mouth tastes them.
202. I turn around once. What is out will not get in. I turn around again. What is in will not get out. What am I?
203. Look at me one way and I weigh a whole lot; turn me around and you'll see that I am not. What am I?
204. What turns everything around but does not move?
205. What is long and filled with seamen?
206. Searing 'cross the pitch-black skies,
     I scream in celebration,
     Yet moments later, my outburst through,
     I am naught but imagination.
207. You are having a bad day if 12 peers deem you to be this.
208. Something wholly unreal, yet seems real to I. Think my friend, tell me where does it lie?
209. I always run but never walk,
     I sometimes sing but cannot talk,

No head on which a hat to place,
You always look me in the face.

210. Often held but never touched.
    Always wet but never rusts.
    Often bits but seldom bit.
    To use it well you must have wit. What am I?

211. A time when they're green. A time when they're brown.
    But both of these times, cause me to frown.
    But just in between, for a very short while.
    They're perfect and yellow. And cause me to smile.

212. What do you call two witches who live together?

213. This food is a white meat, that often goes with salad. It's poultry.

214. I scribble forms of the finest letter,
    And repel elements of the harshest weather.
    I am an arrow-aimer
    and a dust-breaker.

215. More rare today than long ago. There's a salutation from friends written below. What am I?

216. Found under bridges and on the Internet.

217. How do snails travel?

218. Give it a toss, and it's ready, but not until it's dressed. What is it?

219. I don't forget! What am I?

220. I can be short and sometimes hot. When displayed, I rarely impress.

221. Held firmly in the hands, like a sword it cuts deep.
    Bloodless strokes, all, then forward we leap.

222. He has a genie to thank for the fact that he married a princess.

223. Black and scary, small and hairy.
    In the night you hear it preach,
    Through its noisy high pitched screech.

224. I won't break if you throw me off from the highest building but I will break if you place me in the ocean. What am I?

225. My first is equality; my second is inferiority; my whole is superiority.
226. They're up near the sky, on something very tall. Sometimes they die, only then do they fall.
227. It is the electronic version of junk mail or a salty meat in a can.
228. With four oars it swims but it is always at home.
    Its back is like armor, tougher than chrome. What is it?
229. Though not a plant, has leaves. Though not a beast, has spine. Though many wouldn't need this thing, It's more valuable than wine.
230. It can be white or blue or black, Humped or have a horn. And when it talks it sings its menuets, as it's travelling the depths.
231. A certain wizard resided in a city made from this gemstone.
232. One of the few vegetables that is routinely consumed with marshmallows.
233. If you were standing directly on Antarctica's South Pole facing north, which direction would you travel if you took one step backward?
234. I run over fields and woods all day. Under the bed at night I sit not alone. My tongue hangs out, up and to the rear, awaiting to be filled in the morning.
235. Can describe a distress signal or flashy accessories.
236. My first is in blood and also in battle. My second is in acorn, oak, and apple. My third and fourth are both the same. In the center of sorrow and twice in refrain. My fifth starts eternity ending here. My last is the first of last, Oh Dear!
237. What does a cat have that no other animal has?
238. I am the best thing that can happen after a stick hits a ball. What am I?
239. What's large on Saturday and Sunday. Small on Tuesday, Wednesday, and Thursday, and disappears on Monday and Friday?

240. Old Grandpa Diddle Daddle jumped in the mud puddle, green cap and yellow shoes. Guess all your loftiness and you can't guess these news.
241. This thing runs but cannot walk, sometimes sings but never talks. Lacks arms, has hands; lacks a head but has a face.
242. I met a man and drew his name. He tipped his hat and played my game. What is his name?
243. In the evening I'm long, in the morning I'm small; When seen in a ballroom, I'm nothing at all.
244. This is in a realm of true and in a realm false, but you experience me as you turn and toss.
245. What binds two people yet touches only one?
246. I am a place with substance and story, where many masquerade to there glory. What am I?
247. What can get you there in eco style, pushed by your legs mile after mile?
248. I start in little but I end in full, you'll find me in half and complete.
249. A type of hammer that brings a room to order.
250. Ambitious people will climb the social version of this contraption.

ANSWER 201-250:

201. grapes
202. key
203. A ton.
204. mirror
205. submarine
206. firework
207. guilty
208. mind
209. clock
210. tongue
211. bananas
212. broommates

213. chicken
214. feather
215. letter
216. troll
217. slowly
218. salad
219. elephant
220. temper
221. paddle
222. aladdin
223. bat
224. tissue

225. peerless
226. leaves
227. spam
228. turtle
229. book
230. whale
231. emerald
232. yam
233. north
234. shoe
235. flare
236. barrel
237. kittens
238. home run
239. S
240. frog
241. clock
242. Andrew
243. shadow
244. dream
245. ring
246. stage
247. bicycle
248. L
249. gavel
250. ladder

QUESTION 251 – 300:

251. What is never eaten before lunch?
252. I crushed on Wendy Darling. What am I?
253. What becomes white when it is dirty?
254. Put into a pit, locked beneath a grate, guarded through the night, yet it still goes out.
255. I am whole but incomplete. I have no eyes, yet I see. You can see, and see right through me. My largest part is one fourth of what I once was.
256. What animal dwells in water and best known for its work ethic?
257. How can a pants pocket be empty and still have something in it?
258. What can be any size or shape and gets bigger the more you take from it?
259. My first half means container. Not a lot of people understand my language. What am I?
260. What is the end of everything?
261. You row in one while you float.

262. Lots of them make up a word, And lots of words are in them. It's easy when you think about it. A while ago we stamped and mailed them.
263. What is something yet nothing, but if you fill it up it will disappear?
264. What flies without wings?
265. It is sometimes known to have silver linings.
266. Come up and let us go. Go down and here we stay.
267. Commits friendly home invasions one night a year.
268. According to the music industry, you can count on a midnight train and the devil to turn up here.
269. Inside a burning house, this thing is best to make. And best to make it quickly, before the fire's too much to take.
270. People are hired to get rid of me.
I'm often hiding under your bed.
In time I'll always return you see.
Bite me and you're surely dead.
271. What can touch someone once and last them a lifetime?
272. The epic tale of two women battling over a sparkly pair of shoes.
273. I provide cover for games of footsie and tax-free wages. What am I?
274. I make noise yet you don't see me make it. I alarm for good yet sometimes for worse. I have a companion. What am I?
275. What has one hand longer than the other, and goes on all day and night?
276. An artform and its colourful result.
277. I saw a fight the other day;
A damsel did begin the fray.
She with her daily friend did meet,
then standing in the open street,
she gave such hard and sturdy blows,
he bled ten gallons at the nose;
yet neither seemed to faint nor fall,
nor gave her an abuse at all.

278. What measures out time until in time all is smashed to it?

279. What can speak without a tongue and listen without ears?

280. I am a food with 5 letters. If you remove the first letter I am a form of energy. Remove two and I'm needed to live. Scramble the last 3 and you can drink me down. What am I?

281. I do not contain flesh, feather, or scales; yet I have fingers and thumbs. What am I?

282. What has three feet but no arms or legs?

283. I am clean when I'm black, dirty when I'm white. What am I?

284. My first part compliments people. My second part makes things known. My third part hurts feelings. My fourth part holds a previous treasure. My fifth part is used when sharing fancy beverages. What am I?

285. What is the largest living ant on earth?

286. I am round as a bowl, deep as a tub, but all the world's water couldn't fill me up.

287. What has a head and a tail but no body?

288. Sometimes you feel it weigh a ton.
Yet it is nothing, but somehow still there.
Makes you uncomfortable around anyone,
But speak its name and it's gone.

289. It's tough as nails, Or soft as snow. People use it for their rink, Some just put in their drink.

290. What eight letter word has "kst" in middle, in the beginning and at the end?

291. It comes only before, it comes only after. Rises only in darkness, but rises only in light. It is always the same, but is yet always different.

292. I do not have eyes but I once could see. I used to have thoughts but now I'm empty. What am I?

293. You can break it or drink water from it.

294. I have three eyes and only one leg. Obey me or you will be sorry. What am I?

295. The only amusing part of the body. What am I?

296. It can be clear like water, but it burns like fire.
297. A white horned symbol of purity and grace.
298. What is an acceptable act of violence during saint Patrick's day?
299. Delicious but said to be a lie.
300. A big shiny black car nobody wants to be a passenger in.

ANSWER 251 – 300:

251. dinner
252. peter pan
253. blackboard
254. fire
255. skeleton
256. beaver
257. hole
258. hole
259. binary
260. G
261. boat
262. letters
263. hole
264. time
265. cloud
266. anchor
267. Santa Claus
268. Georgia
269. haste
270. dust
271. love
272. Wizard of Oz
273. table
274. thunder
275. clock
276. painting
277. pump
278. sand
279. telephone
280. wheat
281. glove
282. yard
283. chalkboard
284. hand
285. elephant
286. sieve
287. coin
288. silence
289. ice
290. inkstand
291. moon
292. skull
293. glass
294. traffic light
295. You are.
296. alcohol
297. unicorn
298. pinch
299. cake
300. hearse

301. A device that nearly everyone has that can freeze anyone it sees. What is it?
302. This became a fashion statement in the garden of Eden.
303. What is common to eat before it's born and after it's dead?
304. I am but three holes. When you come out of me, you are still inside me. What am I?
305. In my life I must bare, my bloodline I must share. What am I?
306. You might accuse someone living with a stolen identity of being this.
307. I travel in a gaggle. What am I?
308. What stays on the ground but never gets dirty?
309. There is an ancient invention. Still used in some parts of the world today. That allows people to see through walls.
310. My first is ocean but not in sea, My second in milk but not in me. My third is in three but not in throw, My fourth in vow but not in crow. My fifth is in eight but not in night, My last is in wrong and also right. My whole is praise for thoughts or men; Or women, too, or tongue or pen.
311. What do you call a rabbit with fleas?
312. I'm strangely capricious, I'm sour or I'm sweet,
To housewives am useful, to children a treat;
Yet I freely confess I more mischief have done,
Than anything else That is under the sun.
313. This is a shape and a symbol that we literally cannot live without. What is it?
314. I am black and white. I have strings I have keys. I make sound without my lips. I make dough with no flour. What am I?
315. My tail is long, my coat is brown,
I like the country, I like the town.
I can live in a house or live in a shed,
And I come out to play when you are in bed.

316. What bone has a sense of humor?
317. I walk on 4 legs in the morning, 2 legs at noon, and 3 legs at night. What am I?
318. I can help you to mend. I hide my body but never my head. What am I?
319. We dwell in cottages of straw,
    and labor much for little gains;
    sweet food from us our masters draw,
    and then with death reward our pains.
320. I have strong affection for belly buttons. What am I?
321. Tiny creatures that have a special relationship with flowers.
322. Defends your noggin from the hard pavement.
323. In many hallways you would stand, if not with this in hand.
324. In prison I will be found, but I'll never be in court, unless there's more than one. What am I?
325. If two hours ago, it was as long after one o'clock in the afternoon as it was before one o'clock in the morning, what time would it be now?
326. It nukes food at the touch of a button.
327. It's been around for millions of years, but it's no more than a month old. What is it?
328. How can the letters OWONDER be rearranged to make one word?
329. What goes inside boots and outside shoes?
330. My first is in spell, but not book.
    My second is in fright and also shook.
    My third is in cauldron, but never in pot.
    My fourth is in net and also in knot.
    My fifth is in bat, but never in vampire.
    My sixth is in coal, but not found in fire.
    My seventh is in moon, but not in night.
331. My first is a term to relate a circumstance present or past;
    and those who are much prone to prate,
    my second will spout away fast.
    My whole, in the days of our youth,

is what we extremely despised;
and though it say nothing but truth,
yet it never need hope to be prized.

332. Before I grow I'm small.
When I'm old I grow tall.
When I die I give a mighty fall. What am I?

333. In the forest, this blends in just right, but every December it is covered with lights. What is it?

334. To cross the water I'm the way. For water I'm above I touch it not, and truth to say, I neither swim nor move. What am I?

335. I am round. I have only one line. Circle is not my name indeed. What am I?

336. What animal gives away money and says moo?

337. What kind of dog has no tail?

338. I open wide and tight I shut, sharp am I and papercut fingers too. So do take care, I'm good and bad, so best beware.

339. My first is a slice affords so nice; my second discomposes; my whole's a bed where honor's head devotedly reposes.

340. I have four legs but no tail. Usually I am heard only at night.

341. Without coolant, you'll have some trouble with this.

342. What has a bottom right at the top?

343. Where force can't get through, I with a gentle movement do. What am I?

344. Man's most important invention.

345. Though learning has fed me,
I know not a letter;
I live among the books,
Yet am never the better. What am I?

346. I can only be played on a windy day. What am I?

347. A most complex construction,
Of creation and destruction,
Of good and evil deeds,
Of noblest thought and basest needs,
A species in the lead,

Immortal 'til we bleed.
348. I weaken all men for hours each day.
I show you strange visions while you are away.
I take you by night, by day take you back.
None suffer to have me, but do from my lack.
349. Thirty white horses on a red hill, first they champ, then they stamp, then they stand still.
350. I am fun and sad. I am fast and slow. I get louder and I get softer. And I am created by great geniuses. What am I?

ANSWER 301 – 350:

301. camera	325. nine
302. fig leaf	326. microwave
303. chicken	327. moon
304. shirt	328. one word
305. sibling	329. ankles
306. imposter	330. phantom
307. goose	331. telltale
308. shadow	332. tree
309. window	333. evergreen
310. clever	334. bridge
311. bugs bunny	335. oval
312. apple	336. cash cow
313. heart	337. hot dog
314. piano	338. scissors
315. mouse	339. hammock
316. humorous	340. frog
317. human	341. radiator
318. nail	342. leg
319. bees	343. key
320. lint	344. fire
321. bumblebee	345. bookworm
322. helmet	346. kite
323. key	347. humans
324. S	348. sleep

349. teeth

350. music

QUESTION 351 – 400:

351. What shoes should you wear when your basement is flooded?
352. Twigs and spheres and poles and plates. Join and bind to reason make.
353. What is that which, while it lives, constantly changes its habit, that is buried before it is dead, and whose tomb is valued wherever it is found?
354. As I was going through a field of wheat,
    I found something good to eat;
    It wasn't fish or flesh or bone;
    I kept it till it ran alone.
355. I run cold and hot, I look blue but am red. What am I?
356. What can bring back the dead. Make us cry, make us laugh, make us young. Born in an instant yet lasts a lifetime?
357. Prior to smartphones, people used this to record their lives.
358. As I went across the bridge, I met a man with a load of wood which was neither straight nor crooked. What kind of wood was it?
359. I contain six letters, minus one and you got twelve. What am I?
360. What kind of table has no legs?
361. I dance and sing in the breeze, but I have neither voice nor feet. What am I?
362. It's true I bring serenity. And hang around the stars. But yet I live in misery, you'll find me behind bars. With thieves and villains I consort. In prison I'll be found. But I would never go to court. Unless there's more than one.

363. I come in many shapes, sizes, and colors. I stick to many surfaces but I am, in fact, not sticky at all. What am I?
364. The more holes you cover the lower it goes.
365. What has armor but is not a knight, snaps but is not a twig, and is always at home even on the move?
366. My first is in some but not in all.
My second is into but not in tall.
My third in little but no in big.
My fourth in port but not in pig.
My whole is made in nature's way.
For clothing, rugs used every day.
367. What is the thing that stays the same size, but the more it's used the more it decreases?
368. I keep things green and keep kids happy during summer time. What am I?
369. Always wooden and covered in paint. It can make you laugh or hide, because something dark is inside. What is it?
370. I come out of the earth, I am sold in the market. He who buys me cuts my tail, takes off my suit of silk, and weeps beside me when I am dead.
371. This greek dish is similar to a taco or pita sandwich in appearance. It is made with a fatty meat in a taco shell shaped flatbread with tomatoes, lettuce and other veggies.
372. Could be described as the cranium's version of snow.
373. My head bobs lazily in the sun. You think I'm cute. For my face is yellow my hair is white and my body is green.
374. What force and strength cannot get through,
I with my unique teeth can do. What am I?
375. Mouth up it gets filled, mouth down it gets empty.
376. A leathery snake, with a stinging bite. I'll stay coiled up, unless I must fight.
377. Dorothy had a severe disagreement with a woman of this magical persuasion.
378. He is not the skinniest of felines.
379. It sat upon a willow tree, and sang softly unto me.

Easing my pain and sorrow with its song. I wished to fly, but tarried long.

And in my suffering, the willow was like a cool clear spring. What was it that helped me so? To spend my time in my woe.

380. A building filled with books you can't buy.
381. It has 8 arms and lots of ink but can't write a word.
382. Only two backbones and thousands of ribs.
383. It happens when something has been cut with H2O.
384. A third from the sun, and not much else since the world's begun.
    Some may weigh a metric ton. Is a synonym for fun.
    Made a zeppelin take flight.
    A big thing at Isle of Wight.
385. First I may be your servant's name; then your desires I may proclaim; And, when your mortal life is over, hold all your wealth within my power.
386. Holding two swords and eight spears. Dressed in a cow-leather tunic. He peeks through a hole in the door.
387. What never asks questions but receives a lot of answers?
388. I am long and thin and make things right.
    I will repair your mistake but watch my bite. What am I?
389. My first is a title of honor; My second is myself; My first is your and I; My whole is a beautiful fixed star, seen in the winter.
390. What is the thing which, once poured out, cannot be gathered again?
391. Sends paper without using the post office.
392. Whoever makes it, tells it not; whoever takes it, knows it not; and whoever knows it, wants it not. What is it?
393. Used to keep prisoners silent and to make temporary repairs on cars.
394. Where can you add 2 to 11 and get 1?
395. I am never quite what I appear to be. Straightforward I seem, but it's only skin deep. For mystery most often lies beneath

my simple speech. Sharpen your wits, open your eyes, look beyond my exteriors, read me backwards, forwards, upside down. Think and answer the question...What am I?

396. What does someone else have to take before you can get?
397. The ball drops when the clock hits this.
398. I start new then become old. Start clean but be one dirty. I usually start big then become little. What am I?
399. Despite having long teeth, every bit of food it grabs gets taken from it.
400. I am a desire to munch. What am I?

ANSWER 351 – 400:

351.	pumps	374.	key
352.	skeleton	375.	bottle
353.	silkworm	376.	whip
354.	egg	377.	witch
355.	blood	378.	fat cat
356.	memory	379.	bird
357.	camcorder	380.	library
358.	sawdust	381.	octopus
359.	dozens	382.	railroad
360.	periodic	383.	diluted
361.	tree	384.	rock
362.	S	385.	will
363.	magnet	386.	crab
364.	recorder	387.	telephone
365.	turtle	388.	needle
366.	silk	389.	Sirius
367.	iron	390.	rain
368.	sprinkler	391.	fax
369.	pencil	392.	counterfeit money
370.	onion	393.	duct tape
371.	gyro	394.	clock
372.	dandruff	395.	riddle
373.	daisy	396.	photograph

397. midnight
398. shoes

399. fork
400. hunger

QUESTION 401 – 450:

401. Where jewelry pierces your head.
402. Kings and queens may cling to power, and the jesters may have their call. I am the most common but I can rule them all. What am I?
403. The warmer I am, The fresher I am.
404. It has plenty of backbone but doesn't have a let. It peels like an orange but it comes from an egg.
405. It can't be seen or felt.
    It can't be touched or smelt.
    Behind stars and under hills.
    All emptiness it fills. What is it?
406. I have legs but never walk, I may have flowers but no soil, I hold food but never eat.
407. Small was my stature, but my success was great.
    Until I entered Belgium to be handed my fate. Who am I?
408. This thing can bat but never hit. It is next to a ball that is never thrown. It is good luck when found and it falls when it is lost.
409. I can run but not walk. Wherever I go, thought follows close behind. What am I?
410. What do you call a greedy grumpy holiday hater?
411. The French word for 'fun size' in women's clothing.
412. My neighbor makes mistakes. I get rid of them. Who am I?
413. What grows bigger the more you contract it?
414. Though blind as well, can lead the blind well.
415. Oh lord! I am not worthy!
    I bend my limbs to the ground.
    I cry, yet without a sound.
    Let me drink of waters deep.

And in silence I will weep.

416. I climb higher as I get hotter. I can never escape from my crystal cage. What am I?

417. I wear a green jacket on the outside, white jacket as a second layer, and a red jacket inside. I am pregnant with a lot of babies. What am I?

418. A dark-colored creature serenaded by Lennon and McCartney.

419. There is not wind enough to twirl
That one red leaf, nearest of its clan,
Which dances as often as dance it can.

420. Six letters do my name compound;
Among the aged oft I'm found;
The shepherd also, by the brook,
Hears me when leaning on his crook;
But in the middle me divide,
And take the half on either side,
Each backward read, a liquor tell,
Ev'ry gay toper knows it well.

421. If I say "everything I tell you is a lie", am I telling you the truth or a lie?

422. I hide in a dark tunnel awaiting my time. I can only be released by pulling back. Once released, I may do unstoppable damage. What am I?

423. My first is snapping, snarling, growling,
My second's industrious, romping, and prowling.
Higgledy piggledy Here we lie,
picked and plucked, and put in a pie.

424. Seven brothers, five work all day,
The other two, just play or pray.

425. My first keeps time, my second spends time, my whole tells time.

426. Mouthless but I will tell you a name that is not mine, I will show you the years I have seen but I have no eyes, memory I have but I have no mind.

427. A circle of stones, never in rows.
Stacked one on the other, mystery it sows. What is it?

428. I am in the past, never in the future. I don't exist, but have existed. I saw what you saw, and this is what I will ever see. What am I?

429. I'm red but I can be green at times and I am even yellow. What am I?

430. I have 24 keys but cannot open any locks. Sometimes loud, sometimes soft. What am I?

431. I carry my home on my back. I am not rich, but I leave silver in my track. What am I?

432. It is probably the most laid-back member of the animal kingdom.

433. Out of all the celestial bodies, this one has the funniest name.

434. You eat something you neither plant nor plow. It is the son of water, but if water touches it. It dies. What is it?

435. I am part of the bird that is not in the sky.
I can swim in the water but always stay dry. What am I?

436. What has six faces and twenty-one eyes?

437. I can be found in water but never wet. What am I?

438. The athletically challenged spend a good deal of time on this seat made of pine.

439. I run distances, often making many turns, yet I never move one foot. What am I?

440. You seek it out, when your hunger is ripe.
It sits on four legs, and smokes a pipe.

441. They are many and one, they wave and they drum. Used to cover a state, they go with you everywhere.

442. It's held in the hand when going out.

443. I ride, I ride; No tracks are left. I chop and chop; There are no chips left. He rides and rides; Turns around: There is no road left.

444. With three eyes and a black as night, I frequently knock down ten men with a single strike! What am I?

445. People chop this off for a good cause.

446. My treasures are golden and guarded by thousands amongst a maze no man can enter. What am I?
447. What runs around a house but doesn't move?
448. In the fields a frightful thing. Watch it and you will find, it has a pitchfork in the front, and a broom back behind.
449. I am too much for one but not enough for two. Give me to a third and I am gone. What am I?
450. In all the world, none can compare, to this tiny weaver, his deadly cloth so silky and fair.

ANSWER 401 - 450:

401. lobe
402. ace
403. bread
404. snake
405. space
406. table
407. Napoleon
408. eyelash
409. nose
410. scrooge
411. petite
412. eraser
413. debt
414. cane
415. willow
416. mercury
417. watermelon
418. blackbird
419. sun
420. murmur
421. lie
422. bullet
423. currants
424. week

425. watchman
426. gravestone
427. Stonehenge
428. memory
429. apple
430. music
431. snail
432. sloth
433. uranus
434. salt
435. shadow
436. dice
437. reflection
438. bench
439. watch
440. stove
441. hands
442. doorknob
443. boat
444. bowling ball
445. hair
446. beehive
447. fence
448. bull

449. secret
450. spider

QUESTION 451 – 500:

451. I am always with my partner, and I make noise that you never see me create. What am I?
452. I am a fruit with seeds on the outside. What am I?
453. Keep doing me to avoid lens dryness. What am I?
454. I'm very tempting, so it's said,
I have a shiny coat of red,
and my flesh is white beneath.
I smell so sweet, taste good to eat,
and help to guard your teeth.
455. I have a body of stone and a fiery heart, and sooner or later my head and I will part. What am I?
456. This dish is defined as small pasta envelopes containing ground meat, cheese, or vegetables.
457. Shared between two;
Most often to woo;
Sometimes hot and sometimes cold;
The beginning of us all, young and old.
458. Two brothers we are, great burdens we bear. All day we are bitterly pressed. Yet this I will say, we are full all the day, and empty when go to rest.
459. The higher I climb, the hotter I engage. I cannot escape from my crystal cage.
460. I am someone you don't know. Who am i?
461. Its title means book.
462. I belong to everyone. Sometimes make you happy, sometimes make you sad. I will never end until the day you do. What am I?
463. You deal with them and they deal chance,
They show you your future at a glance.
You play them and they play you back,

And win or lose, They go back in their pack.

464. I am neither a guest nor a trespasser in this place. I belong that belongs to me. Where is it?

465. Only one color, but not one size.
Stuck at the bottom, yet easily flies.
Present in sun, but not in rain.
Doing no harm, and feeling no pain.

466. I view the world in little space,
Am always changing place;
No food I eat, but, by my power,
Procure what millions do devour.

467. A metal neither black nor red,
as heavy as man's golden greed.
What you do to stay ahead,
with friend or foe or arrow and steed.

468. Many things can create one, it can be of any shape or size, it is created for various reasons, and it can shrink or grow with time.

469. I am merry creature in pleasant time of year, As in but certain seasons, I sing that you can hear; And yet I'm made a by-word, A very perfect mock; Compared to foolish persons, And silliest of all folk.

470. I have a heart of gold and I smell when I'm old. What am I?

471. I'm the source of all emotion, but I'm caged in a white prison.

472. Hard iron on horse. Cow's hide on man.

473. I can alter the actions of a king and leave puzzled the greatest of philosophers. What am I?

474. Hold these between your knees if you want to set a Cuban beat.

475. His is no small athletic feat,
Has to stay nimble on his feet,
To fight and his opponents beat,
And taste sweet victory, not grim defeat.

476. It is in every mountain, it's not in any hill, it's not in all the world, and yet it's in the mill.

477. If two is a company and three is a crowd, what are four and five?

478. If it is two hours later, then it will take half as much time till it's midnight as it would be if it were an hour later. What time is it?

479. Within passion's fruit they will be found,
and more of them in the pomegranate's crown.
Rowed they are within an apple's core,
yet other fruits have them more.
And though the nectarine has but one,
still, this is all just in fun.
Playing hide and seek - a children's game.
Finding out each player is just the same.

480. I you were to take two apples from three apples, how many would you have?

481. A young child goes up to a wise man and shocks him by asking him "What one thing do i have that God does not?"

482. As I went over London Bridge I met my sister Jenny; I broke her neck and drank her blood and left her standing empty.

483. I am a lunch money thief. What am I?

484. It can cause deflation of tires when dropped from the rear of spy cars.

485. Four years ago, Alex was twice as old as Jake. Four years from now, Jake will be 3/4 of Alex's age. How old is Alex?

486. There's not a kingdom on the earth, but I have traveled over and over, and though I know not whence my birth, yet when I come, you know my roar. I through the town do take my flight, and through the fields and meadows green, and whether it be day or night, I neither am nor can be seen.

487. I am essential to life on earth! I am split into thirds. Two thirds are the same. One of the thirds is 8. The other two are 1 each. What am I?

488. They live only in stories, taller than three storeys.

489. An outcome already written,
Fight it and you'll be smitten.

By it you may be blessed,
Or put up to the test,
And take you places you'd have never guessed.

490. What do you do with a dead chemist?
491. A little house full of meat, no door to go in and eat.
492. It rows quickly with four oars but never comes out from under his own roof. What is it?
493. I never was but am always to be, and everyone looks forward to me
494. How far will a blind dog walk into a forest?
495. A life or death skill for gunfighters.
496. I am a kind of coat that can only be put on when wet. What am I?
497. Serves as a go between in business.
498. What wears a coat in the winter and pants in the summer?
499. In we go, out we go.
All around and in a row.
Always, always steady flow.
When we'll stop, you'll never known.
In we go, out we go.
500. They put the heat in pop tarts

ANSWER 451 – 500:

451. thunder
452. strawberry
453. blink
454. apple
455. volcano
456. ravioli
457. kiss
458. boots
459. mercury
460. stranger
461. bible
462. thoughts
463. cards
464. home
465. shadow
466. sun
467. lead
468. hole
469. cuckoo
470. egg
471. heart
472. shoe
473. woman
474. bongos

475. boxer
476. M
477. nine
478. nine
479. seeds
480. 2
481. parents
482. gin
483. bully
484. spikes
485. 12
486. wind
487. water
488. giants
489. destiny
490. barium
491. nut
492. turtle
493. future
494. halfway
495. quick draw
496. paint
497. middleman
498. dog
499. tides
500. toaster

QUESTION 501 – 550:

501. Brothers and sisters I have none but this man's father is my father's son. Who is the man?
502. You get one if you miss one at golf.
503. For this gourmet style of meal you'll need a pot and some pointy sticks.
504. I have a big mouth and I am also quite loud! I am not a gossip but I do get involved with everyone's dirty business.
505. I count time, but have no end. Tick tick, but I am not a clock. What am I?
506. I am black when you buy me, red when you use me, when I turn white. You know it's time to throw me away. What am I?
507. I have a head but no body, a heart but no blood. Just leaves and no branches, I grow without wood. What am I?
508. What can you always count on?
509. You use it between your head and your toes, the more it works the thinner it grows. What is it?
510. It increases and decreases yet no one see it. It is not a fire and yet it can be quenched.

511. I cost no money to use, or conscious effort to take part of. And as far as you can see, there is nothing to me. But without me, you are dead.

512. When you are a child you are forced to take them. When you are an adult you want to take them.

513. I'm under your face,
I'm outside your mind;
A biological case,
Pressure brings pain sometimes. What am I?

514. Before my birth I have a name, but soon as born I lose the same; and when I'm laid within the tomb, I do my father's name assume; I change my name three days together, yet live but on in any weather.

515. I cannot be used until I have been broken. What am I?

516. Men in skirts blow into these.

517. I am something many people don't enjoy having as a friend, including you. But I am called upon anything someone is injured.

518. I am gentle enough to soothe your skin, light enough to fly in the sky, strong enough to crack rocks. What am I?

519. What is part of you and all around you but if it entangles you, it will kill you?

520. Rotten trees and Jack-O-Lanterns have this characteristic in common.

521. If you look you cannot see me. If you see me you cannot see anything else. I can make anything you want happen, but later everything goes back to normal.

522. In birth I spring forth, in life I unfold. In death I wilt and die, but rebirth restores all.

523. I am easy to see, but no one likes looking at me. Without me, there would be no you. I can make you complain, or make you happy. But you almost always take me for granted. What am I?

524. What goes through towns and over hills but never moves?

525. My first is a heir;

My second's a snare;
My whole is the offspring of fancy;
Which I sent, out of play,
Upon Valentine's day,
As a token of love, to my Nancy.

526. What part of a fish weighs most?
527. I am partially baked. I am not completely lit. I am a portion of the moon. I am lesser than full wit. I am a divider of the hour. I am not a total lie. I am a sibling through one parent.
528. Though my beauty is becoming I can hurt you just the same; I come in many colors; I am what I am by any other name.
529. What animal would you get crossed a duck, a beaver, and an otter?
530. What has no arms, hands, or legs but moves the earth?
531. I see what you see, feel what you feel, and hear what you hear. I know all of your moves before you make them. I even know the moves you didn't make. What am I?
532. What has one foot on each side and one in the middle?
533. A section of the calendar dedicated to mother nature.
534. If I drink, I die. If I eat, I am fine. What am I?
535. If you're on a diet, smelling a fresh pan of brownies could be described as this.
536. I will go within you, and destroy you. Only because you wanted me too. What am I?
537. You can swallow me, but I can also swallow you.
538. What is the first thing a gardener plants in the garden?
539. What is born long, dies short, and spends its life leaving a trail?
540. I am an activity involving pins flying in the air. What am I?
541. What traps a star in its belly but can be held in your hand?
542. I begin and have no end. Eventually I will be the ending of all that has begun. What am I?
543. I am the beginning of the end, and the end of time and space. I am essential to creation, and I surround every place. What am I?

544. Whipping one of these out in the wrong setting is said to be terrible luck.
545. A prehistoric reptile that lives today and the inspiration for the name of a popular sports drink.
546. The plant that is responsible for spreading a lot of gossip.
547. I am blinding at times yet help you see. I am necessary, but you'll burn with too much of me. What am I?
548. This Mexican dish is a type of flatbread made of crushed flour or cornmeal and is cooked and then enjoyed hot or cold. It is used especially in making quesadillas.
549. It flies when it's on and floats coming off.
550. It keeps something that cannot be kept,
And wakes you when you've slept.
It may go slow or stop at times,
But even then it chimes.

ANSWER 501 – 550:

501. My son.
502. stroke
503. fondue
504. vacuum cleaner
505. metronome
506. charcoal
507. lettuce
508. fingers
509. soap
510. thirst
511. air
512. naps
513. skull
514. today
515. egg
516. bagpipes
517. pain
518. water
519. water
520. hollow
521. imagination
522. leaf
523. Sun
524. road
525. sonnet
526. scales
527. half
528. rose
529. platypus
530. worm
531. brain
532. yardstick
533. earth day
534. fire
535. torture
536. drugs

537. water
538. foot
539. pencil
540. juggling
541. apple
542. death
543. E

544. umbrella
545. gator
546. grapevine
547. sunlight
548. tortilla
549. feather
550. clock

QUESTION 551 – 600:

551. Ladies used to party with this kitchen device.
552. I am the beginning of sorrow, and the end of sickness. You cannot express happiness without me, yet I am in the midst of crosses. I am always in risk, yet never in danger. You may find me in the sun, but I am never seen out of darkness.
553. I am edible, pink, and a great summer food. What am I?
554. I belong to you but others use me more often than you do. What am I?
555. What has 2 banks but no money?
556. Gold in a leather bag, swinging on a tree,
money after honey in its time.
Ills of a scurvy crew cured by the sea,
reason in its season but no rhyme.
557. So cold, damp and dark this place. To stay you would refrain, yet those who occupy this place do never complain.
558. My first is to be seen every day in the firmament; My second conquers kings and queens; And my whole is what I would offer to a friend in distress.
559. Grown in the ground, it's taller than you. Strip off the outside, the yellow pieces you chew. What is it?
560. Sometimes I am loud. And viewed with distaste. Poke out my "eye", then I'm on the front of your face.
561. Touch this and you'll regret it. But if it's cold, you won't forget it. What is it?
562. You can build or destroy. Let creativity soar but be careful at night. What am I?

563. At first I am a yellow weed in the lawn, and then the wind blows, and my white feathers are gone. What am I?

564. What is a cat on ice?

565. What comes in many different sizes but is always only 1 foot long?

566. What do you get when you cross a chicken and a pig?

567. I come in winter. I cannot see, hear, or feel. I can't eat, but you can eat parts of me.

568. A small hill with seven holes.

569. What becomes too young the longer it exists?

570. What looks back but cannot see?

571. I fly through the air on small feathered wings, seeking out life and destroying all things.

572. I am a three letter word. Add two more letters and you'll have fewer. What word am I?

573. It is yellow and you can serve it but not eat. What is it?

574. A toasty and crunchy cereal would be pointless without this spice.

575. A tangly game and a destructive weather phenomenon.

576. One pace to the North. Two paces to the East. Two paces to the South. Two paces to the West. One pace to the North.

577. It can be in a hat, Or out of the bag.
If you see it you'll be smitten, 'Cause it's fluffy like a mitten.

578. My first, if you do, you'll increase; my second will keep you from heaven; my whole, such a human caprice, is more frequently given than taken.

579. I am in the sky but also in the ground. When you study me, no matter how long, I will always end with an f. I may be in your yard but not in your house. What am I?

580. I look like a tiny trombone. What am I?

581. I make things short, but I am pretty long myself. What am I?

582. I run through hills. I veer around mountains. I leap over rivers. And crawl through the forests. Step out your door to find me.

583. I have keys but no locks. I have space but no room. You can enter but can't go outside. What am I?
584. If it weren't for these, no one would be aware of Idaho's existence.
585. A single syllable do I claim,
    black was my most famous name;
    Fetal to mortals here below,
    thousands have I slain in a single blow.
586. What holds names and memories which are not its own?
587. What has one foot but no body?
588. When one does not know what it is, then it is something; but when one knows what it is, then it is nothing.
589. Something you do with guests at a fancy party hoping to get a leg-up in your career.
590. What snacks do you serve at a robot party?
591. It carries paper of the most important sort but also plastic, I'm glad to report. What is it?
592. We are little brethren twain, arbiters of loss and gain; man to our counters run, some are made, and some undone; but men find it, to their cost, few are made, but numbers lost; though we play them tricks for ever, yet they always hope our favor.
593. This Cajun dish of rice with shrimp, chicken, and vegetables, is often enjoyed with cornbread.
594. It covers you, you lose it every day and you'd die without it.
595. There are millions of me. I am very small but when moving fast I am deadly.
596. How many letters are in the alphabet?
597. My first brace Nelson yielded, midst the jar of angry battle, and the din of war; my second, when from labor we retreat, far from polite, yet offers us a seat; my whole is but my second more complete.

598. I live above a star who never burns. I have 11 neighbors but they never turn. My initial are p, q, r, and sometimes s. What am I?
599. People need me yet they give me away every day. What am I?
600. You heard me before, and then again. Afterward I die, until you call me again. What am I?

ANSWER 551 – 600:

551. tupperware
552. S
553. peach
554. name
555. river
556. orange
557. grave
558. solace
559. corn
560. noise
561. fire
562. Minecraft
563. dandelion
564. cool cat
565. shoe
566. eggs and bacon
567. snowman
568. head
569. portrait
570. reflection
571. arrow
572. few
573. tennisball
574. cinnamon
575. twister

576. square
577. cat
578. advice
579. leaf
580. paperclip
581. abbreviation
582. road
583. keyboard
584. potato
585. plague
586. gravestone
587. ruler
588. riddle
589. schmooze
590. assorted nuts
591. wallet
592. dice
593. jambalaya
594. skin
595. sand
596. eleven
597. armchair
598. seven
599. money
600. echo

601. Take me for a spin and I'll make you cool,
     but use me when it's cool and you're a fool. What am I?

602. Soft and fragile is my skin. I get my growth in dirt. I'm dangerous as much as pretty. For if not careful, I draw blood.

603. What screams when put in a pot of boiling water?

604. People walk in and out of me. They push and I follow. When they walk out on me, I close up and I stay waiting for the next person to walk into my life when I have a more open mind. What am I?

605. A vessel have I, that is round as pear, moist in the middle, surrounded with hair; and often it happens that water flows there.

606. I am enjoyed with a pot and some pointy sticks. What am I?

607. I can be full, but I will never spill.
     I disappear at times, but return I always will. What am I?

608. I mean goodbye for South Americans. What am I?

609. I have an end but no beginning, a home but no family, a space without room. I never speak but there is no word I cannot make. What am I?

610. Brings the sky a lot closer.

611. I saw a strange creature. Long, hard, and straight, thrusting into a round, dark opening. Preparing to discharge its load of lives. Puffing and squealing noises accompanied it, then a final screech as it slowed and stopped.

612. Though I do not speak, I oft impart
     The secret wishes of the heart;
     I may deceive, may make amends,
     May create foes, and yet make friends.
     The harshest anger I can disarm,
     Such is the power of my charm.

613. The one fashion accessory farmers and hipsters can agree upon.

614. I have legs but walk not, a strong back but work not. Two good arms but reach not. A seat but sit and tarry not.
615. I can trap many different things and colors, ever changing, not boring. Look closely and you may find yourself also caught in my trap.
616. They are the group who manages the winged engines of war.
617. What has a head, can't think, but drives?
618. Other terms for this handy device include doohicky, doodad, and whatchyamacallit.
619. What is at the end of a rainbow?
620. White bird, featherless, flying out of paradise. Flying over sea and land. Dying in my hand.
621. Poor people have it. Rich people need it. If you eat it you die. What is it?
622. A beggar's brother went out to sea and drowned. But the man who drowned had no brother. Who was the beggar to the man who drowned?
623. What age most travelers have?
624. Break me but I'll continue to work, touch me and maybe I'll stay with you forever. What am I?
625. You shoot me but I don't die. You hang me but I don't die. What am I?
626. Surname of the pilot of the Millennium Falcon.
627. I describe a toilet cleaner as well as one of Santa's reindeer. What am I?
628. The signature stroll of ducks and penguins.
629. Round as a button, deep as a well. If you want me to talk, you must first pull my tail. What am I?
630. I moan, I groan, I chase after you. I never seem to rest. Time's up for you. What am I?
631. Where humans breathe liquid.
632. What grows up while growing down?
633. It is an arctic double breasted formal wear.

634. Sometimes you'll find me hard and cold, other times I'm hard to hold, always present in the air, if I'm ever gone, beware.

635. In buckles or lace, they help set the pace. The farther you go, the thinner they grow.

636. Soldiers fight it but never changes.

637. Those wooden birds are now in sight whose voices roar, whose wings are white, whose maws are fill'd with hose and shoes, with wine, cloth, sugar, salt and news, when they have eas'd their stomachs here they cry farewell, until next year.

638. Never was, I am always to be.
No one ever saw me, nor ever will.
And yet I am the confidence of all,
to live and breath on this terrestrial ball. What am I?

639. Some keep it in a dumpster while others keep it in their trunk.

640. Some try to hide, some try to cheat,
but time will show, we always will meet.
Try as you might, to guess my name,
I promise you'll know when you I do claim.

641. Besides Paris, what is the capital of France?

642. A person's greatest asset.

643. It has no legs to dance, it has no lungs to breathe, it has no life to live or die, and yet it does all three.

644. A tower at the root of all confusion.

645. It's in the church, but not in the steeple;
It's in the parson, but not in the people;
It's in the oyster, but not in the shell;
It's in the clapper, but not in the bell.

646. Perhaps the most important adjective for ballerinas and princesses.

647. What surrounds the world, yet dwells within a thimble?

648. The more I lie, the more people trust me. Who am I?

649. It gives everything and then takes it away,

It governs destinies and fates,
It changes and it never waits,
It rules the cards and dice each day,
Is part of any game we play.

650. If you give it a tug, you can sit in the dark. Tug it again and a light will spark. What is it?

ANSWER 601 – 650:

601. fan	626. solo
602. thorn	627. comet
603. lobster	628. waddle
604. elevator	629. bell
605. eye	630. children
606. fondue	631. womb
607. moon	632. goose
608. adios	633. snowsuit
609. keyboard	634. water
610. telescope	635. shoes
611. train	636. war
612. smile	637. ships
613. suspenders	638. future
614. chair	639. junk
615. mirror	640. death
616. air force	641. F
617. hammer	642. intelligence
618. gadget	643. fire
619. W	644. Babel
620. snow	645. R
621. nothing	646. graceful
622. sister	647. space
623. baggage	648. politician
624. heart	649. chance
625. picture	650. lamp

651. They have not flesh, nor feathers, nor scales, nor bone. Yet they have fingers and thumbs of their own. What are they?

652. Someone who is enthusiastic about tending the garden is said to have this appendage.

653. Long slim and slender. Dark as homemade thunder. Keen eyes and peaked nose. Scares the Devil wherever it goes.

654. Who plays when he works and works when he plays?

655. I help to mature your spirits. When moistened I fulfill my purpose. Should I dry out, my task will fail and my quarry may be worthless.

656. I am bushy headed but have no air. No moisture will not enter my skin, but it's good at keeping it in. What am I?

657. You must keep this thing, its loss will affect your brothers. For once yours is lost, it will soon be lost by others. What is it?

658. This crisp stick-shaped roll is often enjoyed with soup or marinara sauce.

659. Both a currency and an antlered male. What is it?

660. What speeds on a track but isn't in a race and has a whistle to announce its steady pace?

661. What word is that, which, deprived of its first letter, leaves you sick?

662. 2 people in front of 2 people. 2 people behind 2 people, and 2 people beside 2 people. How many people are there?

663. Four wings I have, which swiftly mount on high,
on sturdy pinions, yet I never fly;
And though my body often moves around,
upon the self-same spot I'm always found,
and, like a mother, who breaks her infant's bread.
I chew for man before he can be fed.

664. What's at the head of an elephant and at the tail of a squirrel?

665. This food is a staple grain in many pantries worldwide. You often steam or boil it and serve it in a variety of different

ways. One brand touts the fact that it can be cooked in 1 minute.

666. A locked sphere without hinges or key. Break me open and golden treasures you'll see

667. I live in water. If you cut my head I'm at your door. If you cut my tail I'm fruit. If you cut both I'm with you.

668. What can go up a chimney down, but cannot go down a chimney up?

669. Good for telling the future or racking up in a game.

670. At the sound of me, you may stomp your feet, but you may also dream or weep. What am I?

671. This guy crossed a road and everyone wants an explanation.

672. I am owned by every man, though my length differs. Their wives uses me after getting married. What am I?

673. I save lives on the ground and in the air. What am I?

674. My life is often a volume of grief,
your help is needed to turn a new leaf.
Stiff is my spine and my body is pale.
But I'm always ready to tell a tale. What am I?

675. What is it that given one, you'll have either two or none?

676. It is a common and favored clothing material among biker gangs and superheroes.

677. Those with eyes bigger than their stomach will definitely leave the restaurant with one of them. It is named after a house pet as well.

678. I am quick when I'm thin. I am slow when I'm fat. Wind is my worst nightmare. What am I?

679. Flat as a leaf, round as a ring. Has two eyes, can't see a thing.

680. When I'm metal or wood, I help you get home. When I'm flesh and I'm blood. In the darkness I roam.

681. What kind of apple has a short temper?

682. I'm a vegetable that is a long, green stalk. I'm usually eaten at thanksgiving with cheese or peanut butter.

683. Deposit red liquid in me. What am I?

684. Even the oldest ones can be described as current, but a little mainstream.
685. When the day after tomorrow is yesterday, today will be as far from Wednesday as today was from Wednesday when the day before yesterday was tomorrow. What is the day after this day?
686. I always have to work with something in my eye. What am I?
687. The alphabet goes from A to Z. What goes from Z to A?
688. You can break me, and I still work. If you touch me, you're mine. What am I?
689. These women make princesses scrub floors and sometimes try to poison them with apples.
690. There are several different kinds, but the one you pick doesn't do its job. What is it?
691. Everyone needs this, it's great with an 'r' on the end but you're sad when the first letter goes away. What is it?
692. Dark, feathery, and popular in Baltimore and fantasy books.
693. It is a desert oasis where money magically appears or disappears from your pocket.
694. Used left or right, I get to travel over cobblestone or gravel. Used up, I vie for sweet success, used down, I cause men great duress.
695. A path between high natural masses; remove the first letter to get a path between man-made masses.
696. The wave, over the wave, a weird thing I saw, Through-wrought, and wonderfully ornate: A wonder on the wave-water became bone.
697. My first is in fish but no in snail.
My second is in rabbit but no in tail.
My third is in up but not in down.
My fourth is in tiara but not in crown.
My fifth is in tree you plainly see.
My whole a food for you and me.
698. A bird done at every meal.

699. You turn me over after you have traveled far. What am I?
700. A stylish winter top that covers your larynx.

ANSWER 651 – 700:

651. gloves
652. green thumb
653. snake
654. actor
655. cork
656. tree
657. temper
658. bread stick
659. buck
660. train
661. music
662. four
663. windmill
664. el
665. rice
666. egg
667. pearl
668. umbrella
669. eight ball
670. music
671. chicken
672. last name
673. seat belt
674. book
675. choice

676. leather
677. doggy bag
678. candle
679. button
680. bat
681. crabapple
682. celery
683. blood bank
684. river
685. thursday
686. needle
687. zebra
688. heart
689. stepmother
690. lock
691. lover
692. ravens
693. Las Vegas
694. thumb
695. valley
696. ice
697. fruit
698. swallow
699. odometer
700. turtleneck

QUESTION 701 – 750:

701. A salutation from the islands.
702. Upon me you can tread, though softly under cover.
     And I will take you places, that you have yet to discover.

I'm high, and I'm low, though flat in the middle.
And though a joy to the children, adults think of me little.
703. Where is the ocean deepest?
704. For me, much blood has been shed.
I have two faces but only bear one head. What am I?
705. They are toothy nocturnal immortals.
706. Man walks over, and man swims under. In times of war, it can be burned asunder. What is it?
707. What has ears but can't hear?
708. Fred and Wilma's child, named after a stone.
709. I am found by the ocean and offer you a bed.
Whether you want me or not, to your house I am led?
710. Perfect with a head, perfect without a head; Perfect with a tail, perfect without a tail; Perfect with either, neither, or both.
711. I think you live beneath a roof that is upheld by me;
I think you seldom walk abroad, but my fair form you see;
I close you in on every side, you very dwelling pave,
and probably I'll go with you at last into the grave.
712. I let water fall on you while everyone else stays dry. What am I?
713. Vikings use this for warmth.
714. What work of writing can one never finish?
715. You are in a room with 3 monkeys. One monkey has a banana, one has a stick, and one has nothing. Who is the smartest primate?
716. A blind superhero and Evel Knievel's profession.
717. A house has 4 walls. All of the walls are facing south, and a bear is circling the house. What color is the bear?
718. What has a tongue but cannot talk, gets around a lot but cannot walk?
719. Nothing specific, but more than a few. This many clustered, together will do.
720. What is made of wood and metal and must be buried before it works?

721. What did the rain cloud wear under his raincoat?

722. I am the tool, for inspiring many. Buy me in the store, for not much more than a penny. Don't overuse me, or my usefulness will go.

723. My head and tail both equal are, my middle slender as a bee. Whether I stand on head or heel Is quite the same to you or me. But if my head should be cut off, the matter's true, though passing strange directly I to nothing change.

724. What do angels sing in the shower?

725. My first is in riddle, but not in little.
My second is in think, but not in brink.
My third is in thyme, but not in time.
My fourth is in mother, but not in brother.
My last is in time, but not in climb.

726. Four holes, one going in and three coming out; When you are going in you are out and when you are coming out you are in.

727. The cost of making only the maker knows, valueless if bought, but sometimes traded. A poor man may give one as easily as king. When one is broken pain and deceit are assured.

728. What goes up and down the stairs without moving?

729. A huge mythical animal said to resemble a whale.

730. You will find me with four legs, but no hair. People ride me for hours, but I don't go anywhere without needing to be tugged. Jerked or turned on, I always manage to be ready for work.

731. With hands that can't hold and eyes that can't see, she's cherished by some but has no real family. Who is she?

732. What makes my left hand my right?

733. I can fill a room but take up no space.
Look out at night, and I am in no place. What am I?

734. Secured in place, I work undercover, and with a flick of your finger. My purpose you'll discover. What am I?

735. What is a foot long and slippery?

736. It was a tradition long ago,
    When the world was dark and full of woe.
    When men turned darkness into light,
    By mixing, melting and decanting in the night,
    To seek for youth and gold and riches,
    Just to be burned as witches.
737. What do rich people have that can be changed into the law.
738. Silently I drink and dive in fluids dark as night.
    I beat the mighty warrior but never in fight.
    The black blood in my veins your thirst for knowledge slakes.
    My spittle is more venomous than that of poison snakes.
739. What smells the most in the kitchen?
740. Hearing something unexpected or touching a live wire can have this effect.
741. I can be the book one can never finish reading. What am I?
742. What can be played with no rules and no winners or losers?
743. A house of wood in a hidden place.
    Built without nails or glue.
    High above the earthen ground.
    It holds pale gems of blue.
744. My first is second in line;
    I send shivers up your spine;
    not quite shining bright
    I glitter in the light.
745. As soft as silk, as white as milk,
    as bitter as gall, a thick green wall,
    and a green coat covers me all.
746. An accessory sported by many construction workers.
747. What must be looked through in order to see?
748. In addition to the dental benefits, having one of these hanging out of your mouth will make you look like a wiseguy.
749. What needs to be taken from you before you have it?
750. I am the most famous dinner. What am I?

ANSWER 701 – 750:

701. aloha
702. stairs
703. bottom
704. coin
705. vampire
706. bridge
707. corn
708. pebbles
709. sand
710. wig
711. wood
712. shower
713. pelt
714. autobiography
715. you
716. daredevil
717. white
718. shoe
719. Bunch
720. shovel
721. thunderware
722. pen
723. eight
724. soul
725. rhyme
726. shirt
727. promise
728. carpet
729. leviathan
730. desk
731. doll
732. mirror
733. light
734. light bulb
735. slipper
736. alchemy
737. wealth
738. pen
739. nose
740. shocking
741. autobiography
742. instruments
743. nest
744. ice
745. walnut
746. hard hat
747. glasses
748. toothpick
749. picture
750. Last supper

QUESTION 751 – 800:

751. I mirror your actions. What am I?
752. Halo of water, tongue of wood.
    Skin of stone, long I've stood.
    My fingers short reach to the sky.
    Inside my heart men live and die.

753. It passes but you never hear it. Sometimes though, you think you feel it. You think you had it but it's gone. You want to stop it, but it moves on. You lose it, gain it, maybe fear it, but it goes on, forever on.
754. Where on earth do the ways always blow from the south?
755. People in love are often bound to this.
756. A device for finding furniture in the dark.
757. What is drawn by everyone without pen or pencil?
758. I am free for the taking. Through all of your life, though given but once at birth. I am less than nothing in weight, but will fell the strongest of you if held. What am I?
759. These are knee-length formal wear for men popular in the highlands.
760. What word has three syllables and twenty six letters?
761. Some adults still use these to count.
762. It's like a forest without trees, Like a jail you want to visit. Though the inmates did no wrong. You may freely walk along, They're put there so you can see them, Just as long as you don't feed them.
763. I have four legs, one head, and a foot. What am I?
764. Royalty whose bugers are broiled and whose bed is large.
765. Sleeping during the day, I hide away.
    Watchful through the night, I open at dawn's light.
    But only for the briefest time, do I shine.
    And then I hide away. And sleep through the day.
766. It gets passed among men and builds without growing.
    It serves to injure from a source unknowing.
    What is it?
767. What goes round and round the wood but never goes into the wood?
768. When people come for me to meet,
    they come to me with heavy feet.
    The one I hold, when I get my chance,
    will turn and spin, and start to dance.

769. I have no eyes, no legs or ears and I help move the earth. What am I?
770. I am yellow on the outside, white inside, and very appealing. What am I?
771. Has four legs, but is not alive.
772. I am owned by the poor, the rich does not need me. If you eat me, you will die! What am I?
773. I carry you down a gentle stream. What am I?
774. A slow, solemn square-dance of warriors feinting. One by one they fall, warriors fainting, thirty-two on sixty-four.
775. I am killer of trees but people need me.
    I can be blown away by a breeze
    and I have been here since ancient Greece. What am I?
776. Some people avoid me, some people count me, some people just consume me. What am I?
777. You have three stoves: A gas stove, a wood stove, and a coal stove, but only one match. Which should you light first?
778. What can provide food before it is alive, while it is alive and after it's dead?
779. I am a mountain at night, meadow at day. What am I?
780. I am so simple that I can only point. Yet I guide men all over the world.
781. If you happen to wear one of these warm garments around, you might get doused in red paint.
782. He prefers to travel on vines and pal around with gorillas.
783. How many sides does a circle have?
784. They are producers of pies and burgers and are great for tipping.
785. I am wood that is neither hard, straight, or crooked. What am I?
786. My first is an insect; my second is a border; my whole puts the face in a tuneful disorder.
787. U always follow me but I am rarely seen. What am I?
788. Everyone loses us as a child, and neglecting us makes us holy. What are we?

789. It starts at the earth's end and brink,
Filled with water you can't drink.
Has a color, just like ink,
Walk into it and you'll sink.

790. What is black when it is clean and white when it is dirty?

791. I can be found in seconds, minutes and centuries, but not in days, years or decades.

792. I am the reaction after enjoying soda. What am I?

793. They come out at night without being called, and are lost in the day without being stolen. What are they?

794. Brings celebrities into your home every night.

795. I can be simple or I can be complex. I can be found in this riddle or in everyday life. I can be shapes or even colors. What am I?

796. It is the time in your life when you simultaneously know everything and nothing at an instance.

797. What happens every second, minute, month, and century. But not every hour, week, year, or decade?

798. I am a type of animal that hang out in the mist. What am I?

799. What breaks in the water but never on land?

800. It speaks to you, yet it can't speak. When you hold it you can travel, in your mind's eye worlds unravel. And everything in it's a lie. And with every new untruth, still you feel it speaks the truth.

ANSWER 751 – 800:

751. copycat
752. castle
753. time
754. north pole
755. married
756. shin
757. breath
758. breath
759. kilt
760. alphabet
761. finger
762. zoo
763. bed
764. king
765. sunrise
766. lie
767. bark
768. gallows

769. worm
770. banana
771. chair
772. nothing
773. rowboat
774. chess
775. paper
776. calories
777. match
778. chicken
779. bed
780. compass
781. fur coat
782. Tarzan
783. 2
784. cows
785. sawdust
786. anthem
787. Q
788. teeth
789. sea
790. blackboard
791. N
792. belch
793. stars
794. television
795. pattern
796. teenager
797. N
798. gorilla
799. wave
800. book

QUESTION 801 – 850:

801. When I am visible to you, you cannot see me, but when I am invisible, you long to see me. I am plenty with someone patient, but all the more scarce with a hasty one. I am greater than all, but still in the control of those who value my existence. Who am I?
802. How many 9's are there between 1 and 100?
803. I am taken from a mine, and shut up in a wooden case, from which I am never released, and yet I am used by almost everybody.
804. Food can help me survive, but water will kill me. What am I?
805. Every team needs one of these before hitting the field. Get pumped!
806. I am what bring things together. Without me everything you see would be a total mass or debris everywhere. What am I?
807. Responsible for the toupee industry.

808. Without it sounds would not be there, But through it music's ring is clear. It is a symbol for your woe, But only if your name's van Gogh.
809. Bold are the first; true are the second; playful are the third; clever are the fourth; forceful are the fifth.
810. A necessity to some, a treasure to many,
I'm best enjoyed among pleasant company.
Some like me hot, some like me cold.
Some prefer mild, some like me bold. What am I?
811. I am full of holes but still holds water. What am I?
812. A doctor gives you three pills and tells you to take one every half an hour. How long will the pills last?
813. Taken from a mine and then locked up in a wooden case. Never released but used by students everyday. What am I?
814. I am always hungry, I must always be fed. The finger I lick will soon turn red.
815. By Thursday you're over this.
816. What occurs once in a minute, twice in a moment and never in one thousand years?
817. When the horse strokes the cat, the wood begins to sing.
818. Though easy to spot, when allowed to plume, It is hard to see, when held in a room.
819. Used to wield power and glory,
yet results were rather gorey,
When it wrote our human story.
In the eyes of wiser men, it is weaker than a pen.
820. This small, rolled tortilla usually has meat or cheese filling, and was originally invented in Mexico.
821. What can be broken without being touched?
822. I am a beverage named after a stick. What am I?
823. What comes once a day but leaves every morning?
824. I am very large but look very small.
When night falls,
I am cherished by all. What am I?
825. My children are near and far.

No matter that I know where they are.
The gift I give them make their day.
But if I were gone they would wander away.
826. What bird is always unhappy?
827. What is the difference between one yard and two yards?
828. What are you certain to find inside your pocket when you reach into it?
829. Watches students at the prom to make sure there's no funny business.
830. The little pink nub that helps rectify mistakes.
831. *Forward* *backwards* is what I do all day. I come in all different shapes and sizes. I can be scary, and I can calm you down. What am I?
832. I am hot then cold, a liquid then solid, and I am at once flaky and wet. What am I?
833. Curtail me thrice, I am a youth; behead me once, a snake; complete, I'm often used, in truth, when certain steps you'd take.
834. When set loose, I fly away. Never so cursed, as when I go astray. What am I?
835. I have been the beginning of ideas for all time, yet I am just one simple small object, the things that you can use me for can be frustrating and also I can be pretty. I have some of the most valuable thing in the world on me, yet almost everyone owns me. With me you can make anything. What am I?
836. Although I may have eyes, I cannot see. I have a round brown face with lots of acne. What am I?
837. What sphinxes employ and players enjoy.
838. You'll see savory dishes in Hong Kong sizzling in these.
839. What can you blow up and keep intact?
840. Man of old, it is told would search until he tired,
    not for gold, ne'er be sold, but what sought he was fire.
    Man today, thou mayst say, has quite another aim,
    in places deep, he did seek, to find me for his gain!

841. I am the red tongue of the earth, that buries cities.
842. Both peaches and a certain couture have this in common.
843. I can burn your mouth and sting your eye, but I am consumed everyday. What am I?
844. What is big and yellow and comes in the morning to brighten mom's day?
845. What can you never have for breakfast?
846. Environmentalists want to keep this from drying.
847. What is something you can hold without ever touching?
848. What can your pocket hold while it is completely empty?
849. What has a neck and no head, two arms but no hands?
850. Gown but not a priest; crown but not a king.

ANSWER 801 – 850:

801. time
802. 20
803. pencil lead
804. fire
805. pep talk
806. gravity
807. bald spot
808. ear
809. brave
810. coffee
811. sponge
812. one hour
813. lead
814. fire
815. hump
816. M
817. violin
818. smoke
819. sword
820. taqitos
821. promise
822. club soda
823. night
824. star
825. sun
826. bluebird
827. fence
828. hand
829. chaperone
830. eraser
831. rocking chair
832. wax
833. ladder
834. fart
835. paper
836. potato
837. riddle
838. wok
839. balloon
840. oil
841. lava
842. juicy

843. salt
844. school bus
845. lunch
846. wetland

847. breath
848. hole
849. shirt
850. rooster

QUESTION 851 – 900:

851. Two little holes in the side of a hill. Just as you come to the cherry-red mill.
852. The day before two days after the day before tomorrow is Saturday. What day is it today?
853. When it shines, its light is hazy.
     Makes the oceans swell like crazy.
     It makes moods seem more romantic,
     But it makes the ladies frantic.
854. I can be written, I can be spoken, I can be exposed, I can be broken.
855. If it is absolute, it will corrupt absolutely.
856. You will have this response if you would go salivating at the mention of a cheeseburger.
857. I have a neck but no head. I have a body but no arm. I have a bottom but no leg. What am I?
858. I increase head turning rate tremendously for girls at beaches. What am I?
859. What has a ring but no finger?
860. By the way, what never moves, wears shoes, sandals and boots, but has no feet?
861. This sparkling globe can float on water. It is light as a feather, but ten giants can't pick it up.
862. Causes dancing in children when it fills up.
863. Where do tadpoles change?
864. I am a portal to another world which you cannot enter. Only you can see me but I can't see you. What am I?
865. The strongest chains will not bind it. Ditch and rampart will not slow it down. A thousand soldiers cannot beat it, it can knock down trees with a single bush.

866. It can be used onstage or to express admiration. What is it?
867. He stands beside the road. In a purple cap at tattered green cloak. Those who touch him, curse him.
868. They are the shore's gallant knights.
869. Of these things I have two.
    One for me and one for you.
    And when you ask about the price,
    I simply smile and nod twice.
870. I can be red, blue, purple, and green.
    No one can reach me, not even the queen. What am I?
871. As I walked along the path I saw something with four fingers and one thumb, but it was not flesh, fish, bone, or fowl.
872. What dentists battle on a daily basis.
873. Slang for the male half in a marriage.
874. My first is in window but not in pane.
    My second's in road but not in lane.
    My third is in oval but not in round.
    My fourth is in hearing but not in sound.
    My whole is known as a sign of peace.
    And from noah's ark won quick release.
875. Can be achieved in a car or as a position during conflict.
876. An artform and a web-browser.
877. What king can you make if you take the head of a lamb, the middle of a pig, the hind of a buffalo, and the tail of a dragon?
878. What is always coming but never arrives?
879. I use electricity and I killed my father. I am a king. I have a lot of girlfriends, but I also have a wife. Who am I?
880. It has no top or bottom, but it can hold flesh, bones, and blood all at the same time.
881. This thing all things devours,
    Birds, beasts, trees, and flowers.
    Gnaws iron bites steel,
    Grinds hard stones to meal,
    Slays king, ruins town,

And beats high mountain down.

882. What is eaten by man, served among many, grown by many, and white as snow?

883. This baked dish consists of an open-topped pastry case with a savory or sweet filling.

884. What do you get when you cross a vampire and teacher?

885. What breaks without falling?

886. You can't live without doing this, and we all do it at the same time. Yet many wish it wasn't happening. What is it?

887. My first is high,
My second damp,
My whole a tie,
A writer's cramp.

888. My first, though water, cures no thirst,
My next alone has soul,
And when he lives upon my first,
He then is called my whole.

889. I have a long tail that I let fly. Every time I go through a gap, I leave a bit of my tail in the trap. What am I?

890. Sometimes I am liked, sometimes I am hated. Usually I am old, usually I am dated. What am I?

891. What fish came first?

892. What is higher without the head than with it?

893. A white field, and when it is plowed, its soil is black.

894. The leaves are on the fruit, the fruit is on the leaves. What is it?

895. A spent round or a slimy critter.

896. What is the center of gravity?

897. The itsy bitsy teeny weeny yellow polka dot variety is quite popular.

898. I can generate fear
and some say I come out of your ears.
I am as quiet as a mouse
but not welcomed in the house. What am I?

899. I eat as you turn me, my blade cutting wood. When I am full, empty me you should. What am I?

900. I love to twist and dance. Though wingless, I fly high up into the sky. What am I?

ANSWER 851 – 900:

851.	nose	876.	opera
852.	Friday	877.	lion
853.	moon	878.	tomorrow
854.	news	879.	Zeus
855.	power	880.	ring
856.	pavlovian	881.	time
857.	bottle	882.	rice
858.	bikini	883.	flan
859.	phone	884.	blood test
860.	sidewalk	885.	day
861.	bubble	886.	aging
862.	bladder	887.	hyphen
863.	croakroom	888.	seaman
864.	television	889.	needle
865.	wind	890.	history
866.	props	891.	goldfish
867.	thistle	892.	pillow
868.	coast guard	893.	paper
869.	sharing	894.	pineapple
870.	rainbow	895.	slug
871.	glove	896.	V
872.	cavities	897.	bikini
873.	hubby	898.	smoke
874.	dove	899.	sharpener
875.	neutral	900.	kite

901. Neither bought nor sold but more valuable than gold. It is built but not by hand. What is it?

902. Be sure to shout for its answers are weak, but there is no language it cannot speak.

903. I have split the one into five.
I am the circle that few will spy.
I am the path that breaks and gives.
I am the bow no man may bend.

904. What is long, pink and wet and is rude to pull out in front of people?

905. I am bigger than elephant but lighter than a feather. What am I?

906. How much dirt is in a hole 4 feet deep and 2 feet wide?

907. A setting that proved to be deadly for Abraham Lincoln.

908. The artistic vandal's best friend.

909. John Lennon sang about being this toothy creature.

910. I shoot but never kill. What am I?

911. What odd number becomes even when beheaded?

912. Plant whose name sounds like a dish full of dairy spread.

913. His big belly supposedly has the ability to dispense good fortune.

914. When filled I can point the way. But when empty unmoving I stay. What am I?

915. A tiny bead, like fragile glass, strung along a cord of grass.

916. Up on high I wave away but not a word can I say.

917. What you become during a workout?

918. I am the third from a sparkle bright,
I thrive throughout the day and night.
Deep in the path of a cows white drink.
I've had thousands of millions of years to think.
But one of my creatures is killing me.
And so the question I ask to thee,
is who am I?

919. What rains at the north pole?

920. Two in a whole and four in a pair. Six in a trio you see. Eight's a quartet but what you must get is the name that fits just one of me. What am I?

921. Die without me, never thank me.
Walk right through me, never feel me.
Always watching, never speaking.
Always lurking, never seen.

922. Timid or weak people are said to not have these.

923. This Chocolate baked good is a soft candy made from sugar, butter, and milk or cream.

924. I have a hundred legs, but cannot stand. I have a long neck, but no head. I cannot see, and I help keep your house neat and tidy. What am I?

925. What turns from red to black as soon as it touches water?

926. What do elves do after school?

927. What can be seen but never found that only hides in the unwound?

928. Cycle Cycle Cycle.

929. There is one in every corner and two in every room.

930. If you are a man then your best friend will eat this for dinner.

931. Who spends the day at the window, goes to the table for meals and hides at night?

932. What is as big as you are and yet does not weight anything?

933. I love to dance and twist and prance. I shake my tail, as away I sail. Wingless I fly into the sky.

934. I've got a beautiful, beautiful hall all walled in red velvet, with all white armchairs made of bone, and in the middle a woman dances.

935. I am enjoyed by some, despised by others. Some take me for granted, some treasure me like a gift. I last forever, unless you break me first. What am I?

936. The weapon of choice to create the biggest shock.

937. Sauerkraut owes its existence to this head.

938. A man says: "Brothers and sisters, have I none, but that man's father is my father's son." Who is he pointing at?

939. Salty water everywhere but not sea in sight.

940. I go from house to house, a messenger small and tight.
Weather it rains or snows. I sleep outside at night.
What am I?

941. I am a protector of the scoreboard. What am I?

942. I am easy to waste and unstoppable. What am I?

943. Dragons are known to do this to their gold.

944. High born, my touch is gentle. Purest white is my lace. Silence is my kingdom. Green is the color of my death.

945. I can be driven, but have no wheels. I can be sliced, but still remains whole. What am I?

946. Grows from the ground, bushes and grass, leaves of yellow, red and brow, unruly plants, get the axe, trim the hedge back down.

947. I am not very commonly found! Only in some rainforest! I have an odd number of toes! I'm very lazy and hang upside down! What am I?

948. Use me to reward good behavior. What am I?

949. Strip the skin under my skin, and my flesh you'll reveal.
It tastes sweet and tart, now throw out the peel. What is it?

950. I am good at concealing what's real and hide what's true.
Sometime, I bring out the courage in you! What am I?

ANWER 901 – 950:

901. trust	910. camera
902. echo	911. seven
903. rainbow	912. buttercup
904. tongue	913. Buddha
905. wind	914. glove
906. none	915. dew
907. theater	916. flag
908. spray paint	917. sweaty
909. walrus	918. earth

919. reindeer
920. half
921. air
922. backbone
923. fudge
924. broom
925. ember
926. gnomework
927. relaxation
928. tricycle
929. O
930. dog food
931. fly
932. shadow
933. kite
934. mouth
935. marriage
936. stungun
937. cabbage
938. son
939. tears
940. road
941. goalie
942. time
943. hoard
944. snow
945. gold ball
946. hair
947. sloth
948. treat
949. orange
950. makeup

QUESTION 951 – 977:

951. What does a stone become when in the water?
952. Two year-old children who throw tantrums get this nickname. So did the tsar "Ivan."
953. My life is measured in hours. I serve by being devoured. Thin, I am quick; Fat, I am slow. Wind is my foe. What am I?
954. Maritime marauders.
955. I am owned by Old McDonald. What am I?
956. What can be grown without sun or soil and can either provide nourishment or deliver poison?
957. I have a head, tail, but no arms and legs. What am I?
958. What has a horn but does not work?
959. Low on cash? Pick out items from this rack.
960. His eyes were raging, that scraggly beast.
His lips were bursting, with rows of angry teeth.
Upon his back a razor was found.
It was a fearsome battle we fought,

my life – or his, one would be bought.
And when we were through,
and death chilled the air,
we cut out his heart, and ate it with flair.

961. Hoofed frolicking.

962. This food is a tortilla filled with cheese and sometimes chicken before being heated or cooked.

963. I am so delicious that I require a house to contain me. What am I?

964. It is able to speak because it has a hard gone. You know what it is as soon as it has sung. What is it?

965. I lose my head in the morning and regain back it at night. What am I?

966. When it's dirty this should never be aired in public.

967. The older this thing grows the more valued it becomes. It is always much better when its breathing is done.

968. A man walks out of a house that has four walls all facing north. A bird walks past him. What is it?

969. What do we see every day, kings see rarely, and God never sees?

970. You use lots of me, yet right you use me when you're done. What am I?

971. What is it that has a power socket on one end and a corkscrew on the other?

972. When you stop and look, you can always see me. If you try to touch, you cannot feel me. I cannot move, but as you near me, I will move away from you.

973. I can travel from there to here by disappearing, and here to there by reappearing.

974. I am a vegetable that bugs stay away from. What am I?

975. This both describes gorgeous woman and an excellent punch.

976. We are two brothers on opposite sides of the road, but we never see each other. Who are we?

977. This is needed both for courage and hardcover books.

ANSWER 951 – 977:

951. whetstone
952. terrible
953. candle
954. pirate
955. farm
956. mushroom
957. coin
958. rhinoceros
959. clearance
960. boar
961. horseplay
962. quasedilla
963. pancakes
964. bell

965. pillow
966. laundry
967. wine
968. penguin
969. equal
970. toilet paper
971. pig
972. horizon
973. T
974. squash
975. knockout
976. eyes
977. spine